THE MINSTREL

THE MINSTREL

BERNARD BENSON

G. P. PUTNAM'S SONS
NEW YORK

SBN: 399-122-50-8

PRINTED IN THE UNITED STATES OF AMERICA

The proceeds from the sale of this book will in part serve to help the great Tibetan Sages who have so much knowledge to offer us about both life and death and the relief of suffering. They and their people live in great difficulty as refugees since the invasion of Tibet in 1959.

THIS WORK IS
DEDICATED TO THE
LIVING MEMORY OF
ELVIS PRESLEY

THE GREATEST MINSTREL
OF ALL TIME.

FOREWORD

ELVIS PRESLEY had a great gift. He was able to fill with joy the hearts of millions upon millions of people, both young and old, throughout the world. This great force cannot be explained by his music alone.

He looked upon his life as a miracle, his talent as a gift from God, to be used to bring happiness wherever he could.

This story, written about him six months before he was to die, may in its beauty and simplicity be the truest story of Elvis ever to be written.

AUTHOR'S NOTE

MANY ASK the origin of this story...the answer is simple...one peaceful afternoon in Hawaii in January 1977 I sat thinking of Elvis and his music, and this story fell into my mind, so I wrote it.

This book does not shout. It only whispers. Therefore you will have to listen very carefully for it to speak to you. And the more you listen, the more it will have to say to you.

I chose to illustrate it as seen through the eyes of children, for theirs is often so fresh and clear a view.

GOD RESPECTS ME
WHEN I WORK,
BUT HE LOVES ME
WHEN I SING.

RABINDRANATH TAGORE*

*Indian Poet and Philosopher — 1861-1941, Nobel Prize

THE MINSTREL

ONCE UPON A TIME....

A VERY LONG WHILE AGO....

IN A FAR OFF LAND......

....THAT WAS PEACEFUL AND CALM

A LITTLE BOY WAS BORN.....

HE HAD SUCH A BIG HEART....
AND SO MUCH LOVE FOR
ALL OF THE BEINGS..... THE PEOPLE....THE ANIMALS...
THE BIRDS....EVEN THE INSECTS....

THAT EVEN THOUGH HE
WAS ONLY LITTLE .....
PEOPLE USED TO COME TO
HIM.... BECAUSE THEY
JUST LIKED TO BE
NEAR HIM

AND WHEREEVER HE WENT...
HE TRIED TO DO GOOD......

IT WAS A VERY SIMPLE LAND....
WITH ONLY PATHS AND LANES
FOR PEOPLE TO TRAVEL ON
AND THE PEASANTS WORKED
THE LAND WITH OXEN

AS A LITTLE
BOY....HE USED
TO WANDER
THROUGH THE
COUNTRYSIDE
SPREADING SEEDS
OF FLOWERS
WHEREVER HE
WENT......
EVEN THOUGH HE
WAS STILL VERY
LITTLE....

AS HE GOT BIGGER... HIS HEART
WAS SO FULL OF JOY.... THAT
HE USED TO SING...WHEREVER
HE WENT

AND PEOPLE WOULD
GATHER AROUND TO
LISTEN TO HIM.....
FOR HE FILLED
THEIR HEARTS WITH
JOY TOO .....

...AND ONE DAY AS HE WANDERED..
HE CAME ACROSS AN OLD MAN..
WHO WAS DYING..........

...AND HE SAT BESIDE
HIM... AND SANG GENTLE
SONGS .... AND AS HE
FELT HIMSELF DYING...
HE GAVE THE BOY... THE ONLY THING WHICH
HE HAD.... A BEAUTIFUL MUSICAL INSTRUMENT...
IT WAS A LITTLE
BIT LIKE A ZITHER
OR A LYRE....BUT
IT WAS DIFFERENT
FROM ANYTHAN WHICH
HAD EXISTED...

AND WHEN THE BOY
TOOK IT IN HIS HANDS,
MUSIC JUST FLOWED
OUT

AS THIS HAPPENED THE
OLD MAN DIED.... HE HAD
A SMILE ON HIS FACE
AS HE LEFT...

THE BOY SEEMED TO
THINK THAT HE SAW
A LIGHT WHERE THE
OLD MAN LAY... HE
BOWED HIS HEAD, AND
SANG HIM A SONG WITH
GENTLE MUSIC... THEN
HE LEFT.....

HE TOOK TO THE
PATHS ♪♪ AND WHERE
EVER HE WENT THE
YOUNG AND THE OLD..
THE SICK AND THE
WELL .... THE RICH
AND THE POOR ....
FOLLOWED HIM ....
AND HE WOUND HIS
WAY THROUGH THE
VALLEYS AND THE MOUNTAINS......

BRINGING JOY WHEREVER
HE WENT......

BUT AS HE GOT OLDER...
HE BEGAN TO SEE THAT
THE LIVES OF PEOPLE
WERE NOT AS SIMPLE
AS HE HAD THOUGHT...
THEY HAD GREAT
DIFFICULTIES... MANY
WERE SICK.... AND
MANY WERE OLD....
CHILDREN WERE BORN
CRIPPLED.... AND SOME-
TIMES WHEN THE HARVESTS
WERE BAD.... THERE
WAS NOT EVEN ENOUGH
FOOD TO KEEP PEOPLE
ALIVE....

...AND HIS HEART BECAME
FILLED WITH SADNESS....
FOR MORE AND MORE HE
SAW ALL OF THE GRIEF
AROUND HIM.........

SOMETIMES HE WOULD SIT... FOR HOURS ALL BY HIMSELF...HE WOULD ASK HIMSELF "WHAT CAN I DO FOR THE PEOPLE...?"

ALWAYS THE ANSWER WAS THE SAME.....

"SING

BRING THEM

MUSIC

TAKE AWAY THEIR SADNESS WITH MUSIC!

AND WHEREVER HE
WENT.....HE BLEW
AWAY THE CLOUDS...
AND LET THE SUNSHINE
THROUGH

AND MORE AND MORE
AS THE STORIES OF HIM
SPREAD OVER THE LAND....
PEOPLE WOULD SEND MESSENGERS....
ASKING HIM TO COME.... WHEN
PEOPLE WERE SICK ...OR IN
TROUBLE.............

.....THEY WANTED THE
BOY WHO MADE SUCH BEAUTIFUL
MUSIC......

AND HE WENT
EVERYWHERE HE COULD....
BUT SADLY HE COULD ONLY
BE AT ONE PLACE AT A
TIME.....

AND AS HE GREW
INTO A MAN...........

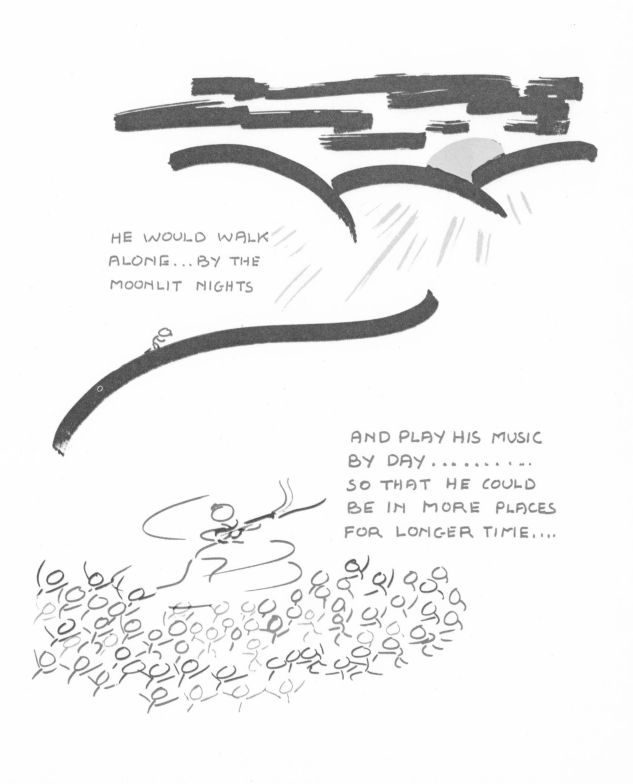

HE WOULD WALK
ALONE...BY THE
MOONLIT NIGHTS

AND PLAY HIS MUSIC
BY DAY.........
SO THAT HE COULD
BE IN MORE PLACES
FOR LONGER TIME....

AS THE YEARS
WENT BY HE BEGAN TO
GET OLD.... AND HE COULD
NOT WALK SO FAR ANY
MORE ......
          AND HIS HEART
WAS SO FULL OF DESIRE TO
RELIEVE THE SUFFERINGS
OF PEOPLE .....HE THOUGHT
IT WOULD BREAK ....

AND FINALLY HE COULDN'T WALK
ANY MORE

. . . . . .

THEN PEOPLE CAME
TO HIM IN THE
THOUSANDS.... OVER
THE MOUNTAINS.. AND
THROUGH THE VALLEYS...

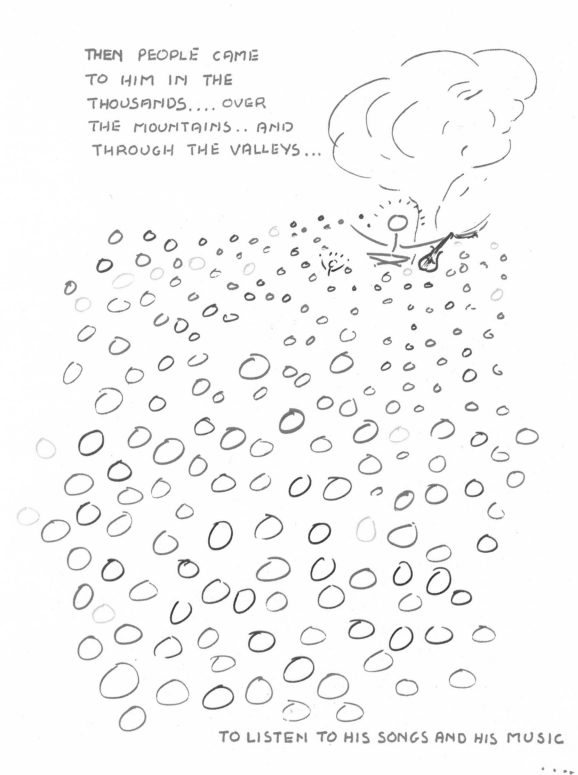

TO LISTEN TO HIS SONGS AND HIS MUSIC

AND FINALLY HE
LAY DYING....
AND AS HE DIED
HE CRIED OUT....

"OH GOD..... IF ONLY
I COULD BE EVERYWHERE AT
THE SAME TIME.........
.... IF ONLY I COULD BE
WITH ALL THE PEOPLE WHO
HAVE NEED OF ME........
IF ONLY MY MUSIC.... WHICH.
SEEMS TO BRING SO MUCH
RELIEF FROM SUFFERING
FOR SO MANY BEINGS................

.... COULD BE AT THE
SAME TIME .. ALL OVER
THE WORLD.... AND IF
ONLY I COULD DANCE...
AND BE SEEN BY EVERY-
BODY.... EVERYWHERE,
WHERE THEIR HEART WAS
SAD................
.... AND IF SILENTLY.. IN
SOFT AND SECRET PLACES...
WHEN PEOPLE FELT ALONE...
THEY COULD SIMPLY SNAP
THEIR FINGERS.... AND I
WOULD BE THERE....AND I
COULD SING TO THEM....
AND MAKE MUSIC....AND
CHASE THEIR SADNESS
AWAY..... OH GOD....
IF ONLY I COULD DO
THAT..... I WOULD
DIE HAPPY......"

...AND A GREAT VOICE ECHOED THROUGHOUT THE HILLS......

YOU WILL! YOU WILL!
YOU WILL! YOU WILL!

AND RAINBOWS BROKE OUT THROUGHOUT THE SKIES....

AND EVERY ONE
IN THE LAND.....
WHO HAD EVER
HEARD HIM SING....
OR HEARD HIS MUSIC...
OR SEEN HIM DANCE.... SAW A RAINBOW....
AND THEY DIDN'T KNOW IF IT WAS IN THEIR
HEART........OR IN THE SKY.........

AND AT THAT INSTANT HE DIED.....

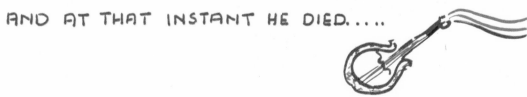

MANY MANY YEARS
PASSED... HUNDREDS
OF YEARS.....

THEN A LITTLE
BOY WAS BORN...
HIS HEART WAS
SO FULL OF COMPASSION
FOR PEOPLE THAT HE
DIDN'T KNOW WHAT TO
DO WITH IT...

HE WAS TAKEN
WITH A DESIRE TO SING...

AND IN THE FIELDS...
AND IN THE CHURCHES
AROUND HIM..... HE
WOULD SING....IN THE
BEAUTIFUL VOICE WHICH
GOD HAD GIVEN TO HIM
AND IN HIS SONGS......
HE WOULD PRAISE GOD...

AND PEOPLE WOULD
LISTEN TO HIM....

BUT........

..... THE WORLD HAD CHANGED.
THE COUNTRYSIDE WAS
INVADED BY ROADS.... AND
THERE WERE AUTOMOBILES
THOUSANDS OF THEM......
MILLIONS OF THEM.. AND
BIG TRUCKS EVERYWHERE

MAN HAD INVADED NATURE...

PEOPLE NO LONGER HAD
PEACE IN THEIR MINDS......
AND SPENT THEIR LIVES....
FOREVER RUSHING AROUND...
ALWAYS TRYING TO BE WHERE
THEY WEREN'T.... AND THEIR
MINDS WERE CONFUSED......
AND THEY COULDN'T SEE ANY-
THING CLEARLY ANY·MORE....
AND THEY TOOK TO MAKING
BIG GUNS TO KILL EACH OTHER
FOR SCIENCE HAD TAKEN OVER...
AND A GREAT WAR BROKE OUT...
MILLIONS UPON MILLIONS OF PEOPLE
WERE KILLED.... AND THE BOY.... WHO
GREW UP IN THIS... THOUGHT THAT THE
WORLD HAD GONE MAD... AND IT HAD
GONE MAD............

THEN, AFTER IT WAS ALL OVER,
STRANGE AND MIRACULOUS
THINGS BEGAN TO HAPPEN.
THE SCIENTISTS...WHO HAD
BEEN MAKING SUCH **TERRIBLE
THINGS** TO HELP PEOPLE TO
KILL EACH OTHER...TURNED
THEIR MINDS TO DIFFERENT
THINGS... AND BY THE MIRACLE
OF SCIENCE

VOICES

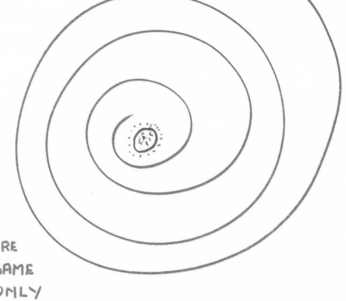

WERE
ABLE TO
FLOAT ALL
AROUND THE
WORLD AND
BE EVERYWHERE
ALL AT THE SAME
TIME...NOT ONLY
THAT...BUT EVEN . . . .

. . . .

PICTURES WERE
EVERYWHERE...
BOUNCING OFF
MAN MADE STARS....

JUST THERE
TO BE PLUCKED...
LIKE FRUIT OFF
A TREE........
FOR ANYONE....
WHEREVER HE
WANTED IT....

THEN A SORT OF A WAR BROKE OUT.....
WHICH HARDLY ANYONE SAW AS A WAR....
A WAR BETWEEN THE FORCES OF GOOD...
AND THE FORCES OF EVIL.....
AND POWER HUNGRY
MEN ARRANGED THAT
THEIR VOICES COULD BE
HEARD THROUGHOUT
THE WORLD.....

.... AND THEIR PICTURES
COULD BE SEEN EVERY-
WHERE.....

AND GREEDY MEN
DID THE SAME....

BUT THE MAGIC WAS
AVAILABLE TO EVERY-
BODY..... GOOD...AND
BAD.....

IT WAS EVEN POSSIBLE....

JUST TO SNAP ONES
FINGERS .... WHEREVER
ONE WAS..... AND TAKE
MUSIC OUT OF ONES POCKET
AND HEAR IT PLAY.......

AND EVEN PICTURES
TOO.....

SO THAT NOW.....EVERYTHING
WAS POSSIBLE

THE WORLD WAS
SWIMMING IN
MIRACLES.... BUT
DIDN'T KNOW IT...

.... AND IN THIS
WORLD THE BOY
GREW UP.........
HE WAS THE SAME
BOY...... HIS HEART
WAS FULL OF COMPASSION
FOR ALL BEINGS....PEOPLE...
ANIMALS.....BIRDS.....EVEN
INSECTS.... EVEN THOUGH HE
HADN'T YET FULLY REALISED IT....

AND HE SANG
    AND HE SANG
        AND HE SANG

AND MILLIONS
    TENS OF MILLIONS
        HUNDREDS OF MILLIONS OF PEOPLE...

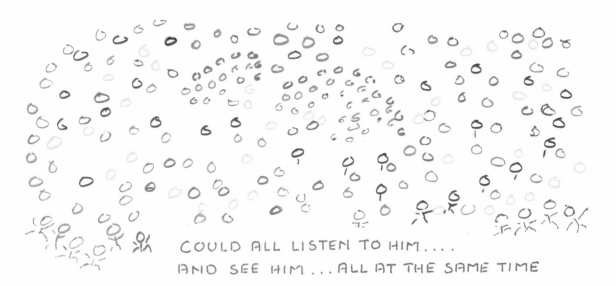

COULD ALL LISTEN TO HIM....
AND SEE HIM ... ALL AT THE SAME TIME

AND FRIENDS JOINED HIM TO MAKE MUSIC....

...AND THEY BECAME LIKE A FAMILY.......

.... SOMETIMES.....
WHEN HE WAS BY HIMSELF
HIS HEART WAS FULL OF
RAINBOWS

AND HE SEEMED TO
REMEMBER SOMETHING
WHICH HAD HAPPENED
TO HIM BEFORE......
BUT HE COULD NEVER
QUITE RECALL WHAT
IT WAS..... IT
ALWAYS ESCAPED
HIM...

AND WHEN PEOPLE
WERE SAD....THE YOUNG..
AND THE OLD.....THE RICH
AND THE POOR...THEY WOULD
TURN TO HIS MUSIC...,

AND THE CLOUDS WOULD
GO AWAY.... AND THE
SUNSHINE WOULD COME
THROUGH....

AND GOD SMILED....

AND THERE WERE PEOPLE WHO
DIDN'T UNDERSTAND....
THEY WOULD TRY TO ATTACK
HIM..... WITH EVIL WORDS....
NOT BECAUSE THEY WERE
REALLY EVIL....BUT JUST
BECAUSE THEY DIDN'T
UNDERSTAND.....

AS HE GREW OLDER,
WISDOM AND UNDERSTANDING
CAME TO HIM... HIS MIND
CAME OUT OF THE LITTLE
SHELL IN WHICH MINDS
SO OFTEN LIVE....HE FOUND
SO MANY WAYS TO RELIEVE
THE SUFFERING OF BEINGS
BECAUSE SO MANY MILLIONS
UPON MILLIONS OF PEOPLE
WERE WILLING TO FOLLOW
HIM.....

....OFTEN HE WANTED
TO BE ALL BY HIMSELF..
SERENE AND CALM....
HE WOULD LOOK BACK
ON HIS LIFE AND HE
WOULD SAY....

"IT HAS BEEN A
MIRACLE...I HAVE
BEEN ABLE TO
BRING...MORE JOY..
TO MORE PEOPLE....
FOR LONGER TIME...
THAN HAS EVER BEEN POSSIBLE...."

AND HE OFFERED BACK
TO GOD... IN GRATITUDE
ALL THE MERIT WHICH
HE HAD GAINED.... IN
HIS MIRACULOUS LIFE...
FOR HE KNEW THAT
THAT WAS WHERE IT
HAD COME FROM....

AND FINALLY HE DIED....
AND HIS VOICE LIVED
ON.... AND HIS MUSIC
LIVED ON.... AND TO
HIS SURPRISE HE FOUND
THAT HE WAS LIVING
IN A GREAT SYMPHONY...
THAT ALL OF LIFE.....
THAT ALL OF THE WORLD....
THAT ALL OF THE UNIVERSE....
WAS ONE GREAT SYMPHONY....

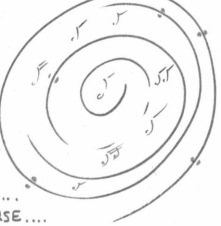

AND HE WAS
A PART OF IT....

AND ALL OF A SUDDEN..

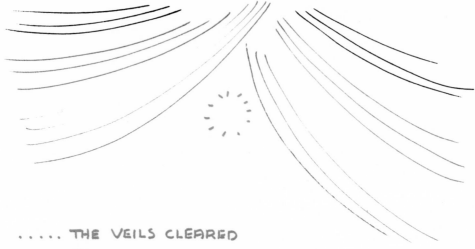

..... THE VEILS CLEARED
FROM HIS MIND.....
AND HE REMEMBERED
THE PEACEFUL LAND
IN WHICH HE HAD LIVED
BEFORE..... AND HOW HE
HAD PRAYED THAT HE
COULD SING AND BRING
MUSIC TO ALL PEOPLES...
EVERY WHERE AT THE
SAME TIME..... AND HE
REALISED THAT IT HAD
HAPPENED ....

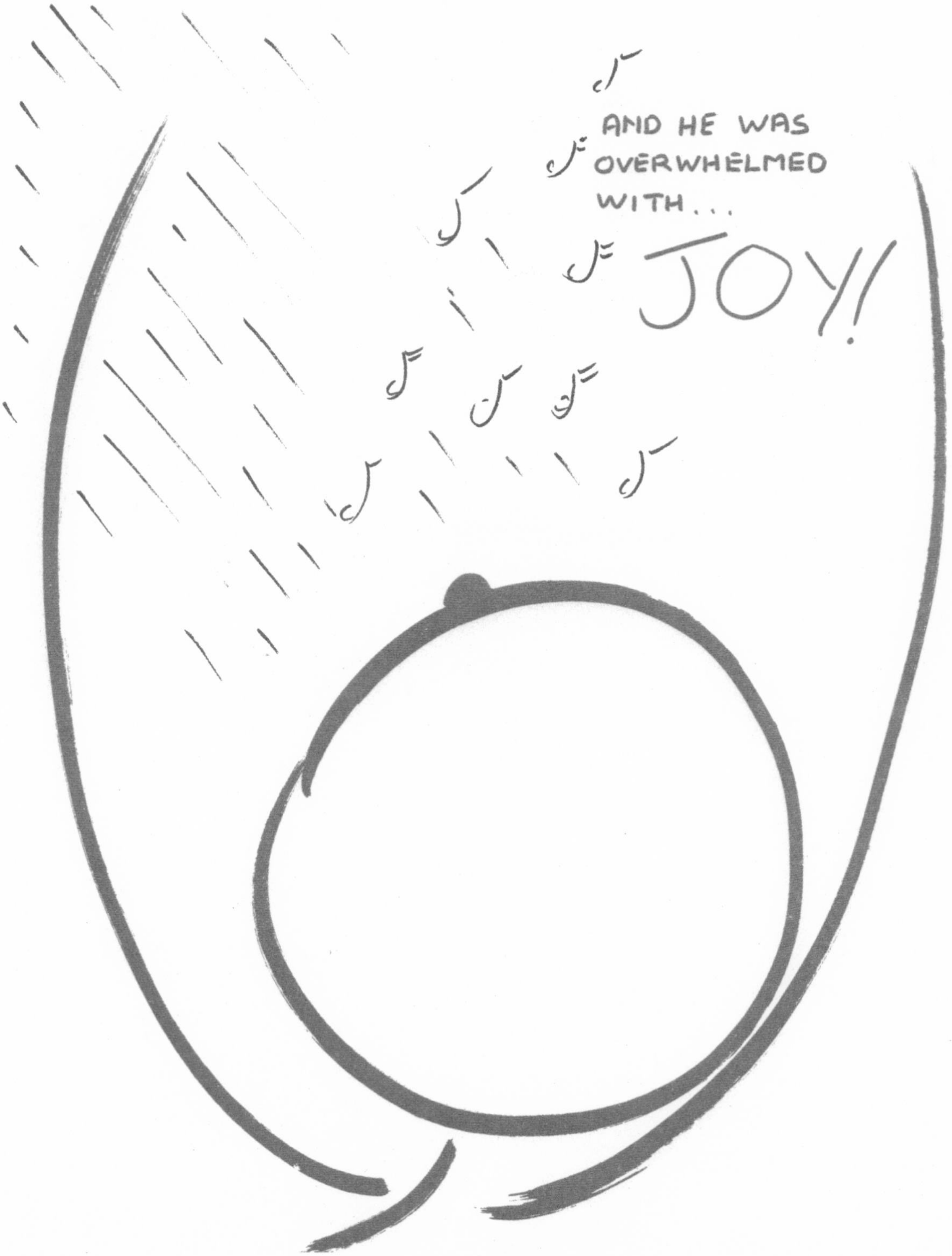
AND HE WAS OVERWHELMED WITH...
JOY!

ABOUT THE AUTHOR
AND ILLUSTRATOR

AT A TIME when people of all religions, and those without, are searching in increasing numbers for the meaning of life...and death, so sensitive a book may come as a surprise from a man known and respected internationally for his contributions to science, however since Bernard Benson disappeared from the public eye to retire in 1962 to his 16th century castle in the Dordogne in France, he has turned his enquiring mind to search, with the help of great sages who already know the way, for the wisdom which lies beyond..."the little shell in which we normally allow our minds to be imprisoned."

Bernard Benson was born in England. A World War II R.A.F. pilot, scientist, inventor, industrialist, lecturer, philosopher, philanthropist, restorer of medieval castles, prolific writer, illustrator. He is above all the head of a large family.

The author has been working for several years on a series of books which explain in a most lucid way many profound subjects which affect the daily lives of us all. These books are soon to be published.

BERNARD BENSON

KNOWING ELVIS was a very individual experience. Each saw him through his and her own eyes.

The following pages are left so that each may complete the book individually with the pictures which are the most cherished.

WHY A PEACOCK FEATHER?

ELVIS LOVED peacocks. He usually had one as his guest at his home at Graceland. His white peacock costume known to millions throughout the world was his favorite.

The peacock feather carries strong symbolic significance in esoteric teachings, for it is said the peacock thrives on plants which are poisonous to other members of the animal kingdom. It therefore neither tries to avoid nor destroy evil, but transmutes it into good, and so is a living example to us all.

Further, the symbol impresses on our minds that marvels can appear spontaneously from elements of apparently insignificant or even negative value.

This peacock feather is offered to you as a reminder of what Elvis taught to so many, that joy, freedom, laughter, tenderness can flow spontaneously if we have the one essential quality...THE DESIRE TO DO GOOD.   —B.B.